BEYOND THE WALLS

Beyond the Walls

New Writing from York St John University

2020

Valley Press

First published in 2020 by Valley Press
Woodend, The Crescent, Scarborough, YO11 2PW
www.valleypressuk.com

ISBN 978-1-912436-42-2
Cat. no. VP0162

Text design by Jamie McGarry.

Printed and bound in Great Britain by
Imprint Digital, Upton Pyne, Exeter.

Contents

Foreword

19 March 2020

I got the email this morning saying Mum's care home had gone into lockdown, 'regrettably… no visitors… foreseeable…' This afternoon I waited in the care home car park. Someone wheeled Mum into the garden and I waved and shouted to her through the railings for fifteen minutes before she was taken back inside.

If I had written those words only a week ago, readers might have thought I was imagining a fictional, dystopian future. Now it is just another documentation of our changed everyday reality. Social distancing, lockdown and self-isolation have crept into our vocabulary overnight and every fiction we live by is being challenged and jettisoned.

The editorial team, then, showed remarkable prescience in choosing 'contemporary change' as the theme for this anthology. Obviously, their choice did not come from nowhere. In a year that had already seen floods and fires, before the Covid-19 pandemic, we know that the issue of climate change is becoming ever more pressing. Globalization, the gig economy and ever-encroaching technologies all impose themselves on the way we live, forcing us to change, seemingly, at their whim.

And the writers herein have responded to these very contemporary forms of change in hugely imaginative, engaging and insightful ways. From an eerie story in which the narrator forges a compelling relationship with an online, box-selling stalker, to one where we can purchase cosmetics to create our emotions, there is a sense of change as an ominous, external presence. In the poem, 'Desiccare', the cyclical turning of the seasons has been warped by human intervention in the climate. There is a note of elegy.

But change does not have to be negative. In itself, it is a neutral word, and has as many positive as negative connotations. Reading the contributions here, this is very apparent. I came back to 'Desiccare', for the kernel of hope observed in the autumn trees, which, despite the onslaught on them, 'still know how to let go' of their leaves. Knowing 'how to let go' strikes me as a very apt metaphor for creative writing itself. Writing is, amongst other things, about letting go of preconceptions, in order to imagine radical, new ways of being. It is an act of transformation, turning experience and ideas into language. We are clearly in a moment where we need to create better, sustaining fictions by which to live. Reading the contributions to this year's *Beyond the Walls*, you will see how writing, and these writers, might help us with the necessary transformations to contemporary life.

Helen Pleasance
Course Leader for Creative Writing
York St. John University

Preface

York exists as a city that blends the old and the new, creating a hybrid city-scape that alters the city and the people within it. York St. John University itself is a perfect example of this merging of matured and modern. The world changes and we are forced to change with it. In a time of extreme uncertainty, we look to things more solid – we look to words on a page. We look to words written by those long dead and fresh-faced alike, in an attempt to give us the comfort we need to get through hard times. Themed by contemporary change, this anthology showcases the talent that York St. John University has to offer, and reflects on the perspective required in an ever-changing world.

Take the step, go *Beyond the Walls*.

Student Editorial Team

The Chair

I heard them talking about you long before we met, I saw the tears of joy, the hugs, the laughter. I watched relative after relative flood the house offering congratulations and gifts and I wondered... wondered when this highly anticipated arrival would occur.

Nine months later I met you, I cradled her as she cradled you and I listened to your tireless screams for attention – for love. I was in awe of how something so small could make so much noise and have lungs so powerful.

In the early hours of the morning I held you both whilst your feelings of hunger were satisfied and then you would drift off in her arms as I held the pair of you in mine.

The years went by and I didn't see you as much but I heard you – it was good to know your lungs were still just as powerful as they were in those first few days of life. The slamming of doors and the thudding of your angst-ridden footsteps on the stairs told me that you weren't so little anymore but I knew I would still always be there to take your weight no matter how big you grew.

I knew you'd hit that age of seventeen when I watched him hand over his car keys, an anxious look on his face as he reluctantly released his grip and watched you charge from the house giggling wildly. I listened as the engine roared, spluttered, stalled again and again... and again.

I was a hostage in the room as you threw your first party, a gaggle of mischievous teenagers swarming the house and bringing with them the suspicious clink of bottles that would have been frowned upon had I not been the only elderly being in the building.

That night you covered me in a mix of spirits; the stains from which still mark me today, and still I caught you, holding you steady as you curled up with me whilst your head span.

The next time I saw you, I knew something was different because you weren't dressed in your usual adolescent attire. I remember you tugging at the collar of your white shirt and rolling up the cuffs of your black jeans, all before collapsing onto me with a sigh. You took me by surprise that day with your rare display of nerves, the dull thud of your fingers rhythmically beating against me still echoes today when all else is silent.

You turned your nose up when she approached you with the apron, burying deeper into me in the hopes of hiding and becoming invisible – like you did when you were young.

Eventually you gave up, sliding away from me in a motion that always left me feeling cold and empty, for I knew these moments of us being together, of you needing me, were becoming more sporadic and I never knew which hug would be our last.

For months I guarded boxes for you, held some even, as you piled them high with your belongings. I was confused as to what was happening; one day you were here and the next day you were gone. 3 years passed and I was left alone, well, almost alone. Some nights she would come to me and curl up and cry and I would hold her as I held you and I listened to her until she fell asleep, exhausted by the emotion.

I will always remember the day you came back. I knew it was going to be a good day when I felt the warmth of the sun hit me as it beamed through the crack in the curtains. Something big was happening, judging by the way she couldn't stop grinning and the fact he had put on a tie. I did a lot of waiting that day, sitting alone in the corner just where you'd left me because I knew that was where I must stay for when you returned.

And return you did; oh how you'd grown, now carrying yourself with the grace and confidence of an accomplished young woman. I watched them hang a picture of you – funny hat on top of your head, gown around your shoulders and yet another important piece of paper clutched in your hands. You'd come a long way from those GCSE years and I'd been there for it all.

There was that boy that you met during your time away, and he'd show up every now and again – sometimes with flowers and sometimes with chocolate, but more importantly every time bringing a smile to your face. I was there the day he asked for permission to marry you, I recall the stutter of his words and the way he smothered me with his clammy hands as the question was put out there and he fell upon me to seek comfort from his nerves.

I absorbed every tear of joy as he got his answer and I soaked up the warmth of the laughter of the room as it replaced the cold empty space I now felt when I realised our journey was nearing its end. I watched them hug and whisper about this newfound secret they shared away from you.

He asked and you said yes and soon enough another photograph took pride of place upon the wall. One of smiles, of a pristine white dress accompanied by a crisp black suit – of love. I remember gazing at that picture and recalling the fond memories we'd shared before adulthood seemed to steal you away from me. After all, that photograph was all I had left since you'd moved out somewhere new and undoubtedly replaced me with someone else to watch over you.

For years I faded away into the background of life; piled high with junk or shoved from room to room to make space for the new. It seemed like all was lost, that I'd even lost myself along the way and my purpose had disappeared – but then I saw you. You came straight to me and curled up like you had done once before but something was different, you were heavier and my creaking old legs were suddenly struggling to take your weight they had so effortlessly held previously. It was such a horrible realisation and I knew it was time to accept that it would be a matter of days before I'd collapse to the floor, never to stand up again.

Day by day I found myself waiting for them to cart me off to the rubbish dump, where I would be left abandoned atop a heap of other unwanted extracts from the lives of strangers.

However that wasn't to be, for in the months that followed I was plumped and polished and pampered even, and once again I saw tears of joy, hugs, laughter. I watched relative after relative flood the house offering congratulations and gifts and I wondered…wondered what this highly anticipated arrival would be.

And that's when I saw you, and just like old times you came to me and settled, only now you weren't alone for the once empty space upon your lap was now occupied by a tiny gurgling smaller version of the girl I had held in my arms from the moment she was born. That was all the confirmation I needed that although life goes on and things change, there will always be someone else just around the corner who needs you.

Erin Abrey

Growth

I decided that I would never cry again
When you held my face in your hands
And joined up the dots
As if it was no trouble at all
How then, I thought, can I not piece myself back together?
How then, I wondered, can I not love her too?

Lucy Appleyard

A Warm Knife Through Butter

We were stalled just outside Burnley. Faulty signal box. Leaves on the line. Train passing through. It was one of those small pockets of stasis that occur without warning or reason, as if to give you a moment to admire the scenery. We waited. I dropped my headphones down around my neck to hear an announcement that wouldn't come. It was morning. The scenery was this: intimate. Like moving through bodies in a crowded bar. The disinterested hull of an ice breaker pushing through a land that pushes back. Buildings leaned in close as if to whisper something important in our ear.

The Wi-Fi wasn't working. I did this journey often and was well aware of what it lacked in connecting me to anything beyond the confines of the carriage. There were ways to circumvent this, I knew, but I took the passive stance of letting this rattling tube cut me off. Out. I wasn't the type to cross roads whilst staring into a screen of blue light, but all the same I secretly welcomed the internet dead-space, beckoning it with a crooked finger as I turned the corner out of sight. Or maybe that's too generous. The truth was, I was ambivalent about the whole thing. I could be connected, wired-in, up to speed, in-the-know. Or I could be out of the know. It was like being at a party where you didn't know anyone nor particularly cared to get to know anyone. You went where the conversation was best. That was a good metaphor for the internet, actually: unfamiliar bodies brushing up against each other in the dark, too much movement and noise and linoleum sticking to the soles of your shoes. The sense of dirtiness. The sense of the thrill. The morning after, wincing at daylight.

In situations like these I would download a playlist ahead of time, a perk of the streaming service that was lucky enough to receive the few direct debits I committed to each month. The playlists would have pretentious names, things like

Here, the sky is always blue.
A balcony. A sky at night.

If not pretentious, obscure. *On the Pavement* was one. Whatever that meant. Some of these were my own, others the curation of another dark body in that crowded room. I was a romantic and couldn't help but indulge myself in these sorts of things whilst at the same time knowing how phony they were. That was the definition of being a romantic anyway, or should be. Believing in two things simultaneously. Afterall, being willing to believe in another type of living meant acknowledging that you were already within one. A friend had told me recently, how when they went to Scotland they spent twenty minutes jumping back and forth over the border. This seemed pretty irrelevant in and of itself, the border being most likely a boring, uniform metal sign, bent or dinted somewhere along its surface, with the words

WELCOME TO SCOTLAND

on it. Possibly splashed with bird excrement. But then the air all around it which was nothing and yet powerful in its symbol. Physically, it was one space. But on another level, centred somewhere around the chest area – more so if you were of Scottish descent – it was two places. Somehow, it seemed to me, that image was romanticism.

I listened to film scores mostly and enjoyed soundtracking the landscape which for long stretches of the journey was a patchwork of fields. Crowds of wheat, if it was the right season. Wholesome farmhouses which spoke of a type of life I had never known. Cricket grounds. A lone golf course, a plump man teeing up for a shot I would never witness. One particular muddy spot where couples in wellington boots liked to walk their spaniels. Occasionally I would time the journey to catch sunset fall over these slow spaces that fell between the fast ones like the gap between heart beats, the landscape's blood moving like a swollen, glossy river. But my headphones were around my neck, and I was waiting for a crackle to leak out of the tannoy. The view turned a little sharper without the music to soften it. Nothing was being turned into something grander than it was, it was just being itself. A building ahead stood close by on the right, like an interloper. A wayward tree. It was made from that familiar Yorkshire stone, old and dilapidated. Painted in white across its facade in uneven, wavering letters:

EYESORE

I thought the locals had branded it. A victim of the gentrification of northern industrial towns – not big enough to be refurbished into office space for hip brands, too close to the tracks to be viable for transformation into luxury flats. We were still waiting. The ticker attached to the ceiling read only a string of dots, a never-ending ellipsis. I shuffled in my seat, bent my neck left and right. I looked back at the building, hands on my headphones, about to replace them around my head. And then it occurred to me, just a hint really, a back-of-the-neck feeling, that we were the ones being accused. I noted the building's angle, twisted just so, like a board on a pavement turned to catch the most eyes. My eyes.

E Y E S O R E

Oh, I think. Oh.

It was hard not to take it personally, not to feel the shame of knowing that I had been branded. Or if not me the space in which I currently existed, a space that ferried passengers laterally across the country. This route that had ground itself into the landscape for the last 172 years, or so. It was easy, I thought, to look out of the window and think the world as sweet as ever when you were the one cutting through it. It was as easy as a warm knife through butter. Boot on ant. I had the desperate urge to slide down in my seat. To look the other way and pretend I hadn't noticed.

Later I would Google this route, the Calder Valley line, and Wikipedia the history. I would put a pouch of 2 minute rice in the microwave, note that the plastic was not currently widely recycled, and refresh the BBC News app. Distant government figures would approve plans to use hawks to discourage birds from nesting in woods that lay, though they didn't know it yet, in the path of HS2. For a moment, the image in my head would be of a tree strapped to a set of tracks, and there would be a noise gradually getting louder, and a sense that something was coming. The world about to be bruised again, blood vessels of movement bursting across its surface. Back gardens and living rooms run through by the blurred faces of strangers behind glass. Bones brought up in the night. Then the microwave would beep, I would lock my phone, and burn my fingers on the steam escaping the plastic. And this is how it is always happening, I would think, we are always looking at things and looking away.

Change [redacted]

All aboard the slag heap of change –
stand by and watch
as the top meets the bottom
and all equals out;
stand up and stand back
as molten progress threatens
the safety of your three-figured shoes,
as kids in China and India and poor old Taiwan
rise up and rise against the torrents
of a capital gain
from a not so capital idea.

But beware this fallacy as just that –
as kids in China and India and poor old Taiwan
try to rise up but fall back,
deficient bones breaking under
deficiencies of kindness
as the thin-lipped
walking suits of Wall Street
fall to their own knees,
as numbers on screens drop
whilst the number of screams
drop upon deaf ears, hearing nothing
but silence.

Tod Barnbrook

Why pigeons must suffer for pigs

Singing? No, the Pigeons scream.
Screaming.
To capture the attention of the cock-
rul…
Those specific dic-
tator that eats and feeds a nation of hungry ass;
holes are dug.
Graves are set for those who have wronged them.
They decide who's wrong and right; the tw –
at those who stood against them, why?

The pigeons, the "skum".
Their (s)cum, shooting at us.
Plated armour, creamy white.
Slurs are strung on, hidden between
sentences, lived out behind bars
by people who need guidance,
killed because of their skin and their sin –
show me why.
Why pigeons must suffer for pigs?

Sophie Barrett

Baby

The baby's cry in the distance breaks through your skull, piercing your ears harder than the blow to the face you'd just received. It stings like a burn, the contact of her skin on your already tender cheek sends you spinning towards the countertop which is littered with empty vodka bottles, paracetamol packets and toast crumbs. You can smell her cigarette at the back of your throat… like an ash flavoured lozenge lodged between your tonsils.

She is in the fridge now, reaching for the bottle of red you had presented her with the morning before, she didn't even debate a glass these days. You hear the baby again, but it's soon interrupted by the shaking of the floor under your feet from the sheer force of the fridge door being slammed. An egg cracks. Her lips find the cigarette again, taking an exaggerated draw before she rubs the end into the skin on your palms. You don't scream, you don't move. You hear the sizzle, almost like steak on a hot plate grill, and soon the smell of ash is replaced by the peculiar coppery smell you know to be your burning flesh.

Before you can even flinch from the pain she's gone, and the baby is no longer screaming. Your head is swimming… the feeling of blood rises up to your ears… nose… eyes, you're surprised when your tears aren't as red as that bottle of wine. You realise you're on the floor, fingernails gripping the countertops as you try to haul yourself up from the tiles. You try so hard to pull yourself up you break a nail clean off. It falls between a crack in the tiles you're certain your head caused.

Blood. You're bleeding. Focus. *STAND UP*, you tell yourself.

You realise the baby monitor has been discarded on the floor, the antenna snapped into three neat little pieces. That's the second one this month. Somewhere distant the baby is still crying. PULL YOURSELF TOGETHER. You drag yourself to your bedroom, and upon passing the living room find her wrapping some form of tourniquet around the top of her bicep. She flicks the tip of the needle before inserting it, her eyes trembling into the back of her head. She gives herself bruises now too.

Do you pack a bag? Forget the bag. The baby. Milk? The baby breastfeeds. Money? You don't work, you're too fragile these days. She receives the benefits. How do you look after a baby? HOW DO YOU LOOK AFTER A BABY?

You're in your bedroom now. The baby's face is so red, so snotty, so wet. It's sobbing, the sort where it's breath hitches and you worry whether it'll catch it again. It gets stuck on an inhale, a sharp gasp and you can see it's tonsils shaking. *Shhh* you say. *Shh...* then *SHOOT!* You blow on the baby's face, pick it up, and hold it to your racing chest, you squeeze it like you've never held it before, swaying back and forth like you've seen the women on TV do millions of times. *Daddy's here.* The baby begins to sob again. Relief. You feel it's chest rising next to yours.

You're dripping wet and the baby is still shaking. You grab a stained blanket off the bed and wrap it round it's tiny body. You recognise the bag on the side that you use when you take the baby outside, it's black exterior is covered in tiny animals, a large, cream, peaceful looking sheep embroidered in the middle. You put the baby down before reaching across the crumpled sheets to grab it.

I'll use it to pack the baby's...

Before you know it you're out cold. Your eyes too heavy to lift. There's a second where you're aware you have gone, your mind is still there but your vision has faded. People say your life flashes before your eyes when you're about to die, yet you see nothing. No life, every single memory ripped away from you by someone you swore your life away to. You see nothing but her ten years ago, on your wedding day. That beautiful, porcelain face smiling up as you as you slide her ring onto a finger you'd have given anything to touch again. These days she felt different, you hadn't held her hands in months, but the last time you felt nothing but flesh and bone. Your last thought was a day that felt decades away. How could things change so much in such a short space of time?

When you finally wake up you see red. It feels like hours but the clock claims it's been minutes... it's ticking seems to mock you, it's in time with the throbbing in your head, yet slower than your heart rate. You clutch the bag in your hand, the sheep on the side now seems to be smirking. *You think you can run so easily?* You hear her footsteps, irregular and loud, pounding. Pounding along with the clock, pounding along with your heart, pounding along with the throbbing in your chest, pounding along with the baby's shallow breaths. She's getting closer and as she does, your vision clears. Your mind clears. You allow four more steps before you grasp the baby tighter. Another three and you open the window. Another two and you're climbing over the ledge, the cold air hitting you both almost as hard as she does. Relief fills your chest as the final step you anticipate never comes.

This Was Our Land

I wish I could fix the world
all on my own.
If only so I could sleep
at night, instead of conquering
fires of anxiety
that burn my eyelids, forcing me
to wake to thoughts of how we failed.

In rare dreams, I shoot
for the moon, I hope for the stars.
Then, I evaporate at the edge
of a deconstructing atmosphere –

Did they tell you that could happen?

Even if all the streetlights faded
for one illicit night,
reality glares all too brightly
refracting through plastic.
The darkness could never hide us:

Monsters of Humanity.

Lottie Brooke

Girl to Woman

There's a little girl,
resting inside of me ever so peacefully,
who if given the chance would leap
out of my soul.
She'd dance to her own tune.
Laugh at anything she wanted
or hum her way round Tesco's.
Not a care in the world.
She'd eat all the sweets
without worrying about fillings.
She'd wear blue tights, a pink tutu,
and not give a damn.
That little girl would trust
anyone and everyone apart from
stranger danger.
She'd be so happy.
That little girl was me.
Was.

The woman I have become fights
to get through the workday,
whilst sleep deprived.
She doesn't hum round Tesco's,
she stresses and budgets.
She cries at her workload.
Gets up in the morning and
drowns in caffeine,
as a coping mechanism.
It's not all rainy.
There's days when I find joy;
in finding a new book,
spending time with friends,
or rather my cats.
I dance round my house
and hum as I work.
There was a little girl now,
She's a powerhouse of a woman.

Abbi
Davison

Blossom in January

The trees were covered in blossom,
looking like sticks of candy floss,
or soft snowflakes,
or confetti
waiting to fall,
but it was January.

Go away, I told the petals, *you shouldn't be here*
but we are here, they replied
three months too early, I said, *go away*
no, the petals said, *you put us here*
you, who choked the seas with plastic
you, who filled the skies with poison
you, who emptied the earth of goodness
you put us here.

Even through the storms,
the candy floss petals clung
to the tree, sickly sweet.

Olivia Fyfe

Let Go

Memories are all I have left.
Days spent running in fields
Back to grandma's homemade jam tarts
Stung to hell by nettles.
But we never cared.

Daffodils invade her idyllic garden.
In the middle of it all an apple tree
Where we swung for hours at a time,
Trying to bat apples,
As far over the hedge beyond
Where we could care.

There used to be a sandbox for a good few years,
We got rid of it after grandma died
Because no one would refill it with sand.
Though I never cared for it,
After that time, you threw sand into my eye.

I'd always wander past the holly bushes
To uncharted territories
Where any monster could dwell.
But I would go on fearlessly,
Holly pricking my bare feet.

Camping in the back garden,
Playing badminton,
The garden was my escape.
Somewhere I knew and cared for.
But it's gone.

We drive past the house,
I always wonder who lives there now,
Who has changed my memories?   *Catherine*
I don't want to go back there,   *Gent*
Rather, I wish to go back to my memories.

Daughter Dearest

David took a deep breath. He didn't know why he was nervous. He was always confident. He never had to worry about himself falling shy, never had to apologise for anything. He had a high paying job and was regarded as an upstanding citizen. He adjusted his black tie and straightened his suit as he looked in the mirror.

'I'm a confident person, I'm tough as nails! I don't need to be this worried about a child!'

He tried to make himself seem more confident to his reflection. Perhaps if he convinced himself that he was still a person in high regard, he could convince his daughter too.

She walked down the street thinking to herself; *It's been so long, I wonder if he actually cares at all.* She looked across the street and focused on the parents playing with their children. 'At least mom was around to do that with me' she whispered as she smiled to herself, rounding the corner towards a sleek looking restaurant where she would be meeting her father for the first time in years. When she entered the restaurant, she was incredibly surprised to see that her father had lived up to his promise.

Without needing to look around, he was able to sense her standing not too far behind him. He could tell by looking at her face that she was terrified, curious and sad. Little did she know that he was feeling all of these emotions too. David softened his features and welcomed his daughter over.

'Hey, sweetheart.'

'Hey, Dad,' she spoke softly. 'It's been a long time.'

'I know.' He sat down at the table alongside her. 'So... how've you been?'

She looked at her father and thought about all the years she had without him. Though she loved her mother and the years without David had been fun and normal, she couldn't help but feel as if she wished she could turn back time and see him more often.

'I've been fine, Mum too. School was fine, I mean I managed to graduate so...' She chuckled a little which made David smile, knowing that his daughter had been happy and had a good life.

'What about you Dad? How's your life been?'

David had to pause and think for a moment. He didn't know if she knew about his life since leaving her mother, the fact that he had not known that she was his until his ex had told him that the little girl was his all along. She noticed this pause and came clean.

'Dad?' He looked directly at her.

'I know about everything. Everything to do with Mum and why you left in the first place. Mum eventually told me the truth. I don't care really. I'm just glad that you actually wanted to see me.' He had stared at her with a surprised face, softening into a smile that twinned with his daughter.

They really were like father and daughter at that point, both having the same smile and the same eyes that could read the other in an instant.

'I'm glad your mother told you. Now there won't be any secrets between us.'

'I'm glad too.' She paused, the soft smile never fading. There was a silence again. This time filled with hope and change. 'I was wondering, would it be possible for us to get to know each other better? I mean, if you wanted to that is?'

David had been surprised again, but this quickly formed into a grin that stretched from ear to ear. He leapt from his seat, knocking it to the ground, and hugged his daughter much to her surprise. As soon as his arms wrapped around his little girl, he began to sob. No longer was David the man only built from confidence and strength but was now the strong, confident, caring and loving father that his daughter could still look up to even though she was all grown up.

Three Years Later

She looked absolutely stunning in her dress. Like an angel that fell from Heaven. He couldn't bear to let her go, not after he had finally gotten to know everything about her; her likes and dislikes, what she wanted to be when she grew up and how she got to be where she is now. But she was a grown woman who had managed to find the most wonderful partner that loved her like the Prince loved the Princess in all of the fairy tales told before. He couldn't help it, he shed a tear for his little Princess. He was letting her go, this time in the right way. He kissed her cheek and smiled as he handed her over to her husband to be. He shook his hand, shed another tear and kept smiling.

A high-pitched amalgamation of laughter and a scream filled the air as the stamping of tiny feet zoomed across the hardwood flooring. David smiled as his granddaughter came running at him at full speed. Opening his arms wide, he scooped her up and held her tight, like he would never let her go.

'Oh sweetheart, I've missed you so much!' David exclaimed. His granddaughter just giggled uncontrollably in his arms. *Click-flash.* He looked up and saw his son-in-law holding a camera, beside him, his daughter smiling that brilliant smile that she showed the first time they met. That smile had never faded from the family. His granddaughter had the same smile, she looked so much like her mother. Feeling small hands tug at his own, he followed the tiny girl out to the garden where multi-coloured flowers and lush green bushes grew. There was a small blanket laid out in the middle of the garden, several toys were strewn across it. The little girl had created a setting all too familiar to David. It was set up just like the restaurant. The very moment that he met his daughter dearest. The moment that changed his life for the better.

*

David never thought the he would be capable of loving someone so deeply that he would do anything for them. He loved every single minute of being a father, a grandfather and part of a loving family. Looking down at everything, he spotted his granddaughter straight away, who at 8 years old had accomplished so much. He wished he could be there to hold her and dry her tears, instead he smiled down upon her, wishing that the fates would allow her to have her best chance at life. She had gone above and beyond, whatever walls came her way, she would be able to climb over with ease.

All because of one simple change.

Chloe Green

Nostalgia

… of a time when life was a joy,
waiting eagerly to unwrap
each new toy, summer days where
the corner shop was infinity
and a bike could fly you to the moon.
Such a pity.

… of a time before lemonade became gin,
and you only cared about the playground
wars you wanted to win. Boys and girls were
as they were, no one was ripped
apart and a person became your friend
instead of baiting your heart.

… of a time where kisses were a thing
you'd never expect,
not now in this wicked game
we call sex. When all genders
were safe to walk alone
in the dark.

Now it's all changed.
Now it's such a ludicrous lark.

… of a time where shrapnel could buy
you the world, before the truth
was unfurled.
When drugs were nothing
more than a sweet syrup, now life's
a bitter taste, our feet no longer
in the stirrups.

(cont.)

... of a time when nowhere was safer
than the arms of your mother,
when the love of your father
ensured no harm from another.
Infinity was within our mind,
but not anymore.

Now the world is leaving us behind.
And all we wanted to do
was grow up.

Georgia Haines

Like Son, Like Father

'A truly real Irishman, a giolla gan ceann.'
— Paul Durcan

Finbarr Silvestre saw life through the bottom of a glass. A retired nationalist with the head of snowflake; he had an arm like a leg and a punch that could sink a battleship. The only problem for him was that his head just didn't sit quite right on his shoulders. It just wouldn't do. He had to get a new one and his doctor agreed. Lucky for Finbarr, his let-down-of-a-son had one up for grabs that wasn't being put to any moral use. So, as any father would, he took it. In short, he was a good man who did bad things.

Bad things he did:
• Missed church (every week)
• Made up words
• Pissed in the street
• Took his dying son's head (he was about to kick the bucket anyway)
• Drank 10 pints a day
• Drank too much and *then* pissed in the street

'I'm a good man,' he would tell the tapster behind the bar whenever one of these things came up in conversation. It seemed to find its way into the conversation a tad too often for old Finbarr's liking. Things were different these days, though; he had a new head and people were starting to notice.

One afternoon, on his usual trail down Falls Road, he was met short by a preacher who must have had a death wish.

'How dare you?' the man mumbled, keeping just the right amount of distance for his own good.

'Be away, pontiff. He had no use of this head. Now, if you don't mind, I have important business to attend to,' Finbarr explained, and moved along without looking back.

100 yards further down the road and he was stopped midstream again, this time by an old merchant he often saw passing by.

'Hey you,' he called. 'You ought to be ashamed!'

'I ought to be 3 pints deep, but unfortunately, I keep getting disturbed. Besides, thingamajig is 6 feet under and I've got a life to live.'

He picked up the pace for the pub was now in sight. Before he reached his beloved O'Tooles, he stopped for a piss. He was draining like a race horse when he felt a strong, firm tap on his shoulder. He turned on a sixpence and almost drenched the guy.

'What the feck, do you mind?' Finbarr said.

The stranger didn't flinch. 'I'm a friend of Ginger's. You call yourself a father!'

Finbarr had had just about enough; no more words were exchanged as he tucked away his master of ceremonies. The boy was left kaput and Finbarr set off once more, reaching O'Tooles seconds after. In the days of that nonagenarian head he carried for near 60 years, he would have chuckled at the events that arose down Falls Road that afternoon. Today though, finally sitting with his handsomely poured stout, he couldn't help but feel guilt-ridden. He hoped to God this new head wasn't allergic to the black stuff.

Two weeks went by and things were getting worse, but he still continued with his same humdrum routine, all the while ignoring the glare of onlookers. He was persistent. He continued drinking his stout, hoping he could regain the taste. It proved no use. Even the whiskey tasted off. He looked toward the tapster through his son's eyes.

'Do I seem different to you?' he asked.

'Well I didn't want to say, but you've never been the same since that dreaded transplant.'

'I don't want to change; I like the way I am... Maybe it's this whiskey... whiskey is the devil.'

'Go get it checked, better safe than sorry,' suggested the trusty tapster.

So, Finbarr did just that. One to one, the specialist told him with absolute confidence that the transplant had been a success.

'You are the same old feared man, just slightly younger and a lot more ginger,' he declared. 'Oh, and you've shrunk by two inches... but it's nothing to worry about. Take my word for it.'

As far as he was concerned, he had no reason to ask any more questions on the matter and went away feeling much more chipper in time for his afternoon crawl. Unfortunately, before he could even leave the door for O'Tooles, his cheerfulness was overtaken. He felt a slight twinge of his senses. The skin on his body began to get whiter. Changing. Dying and growing at the same time. Rushing to find his reflection, he saw his son's face staring back at him. It would never have been his first choice, but here he was, watching this somatic change unfold. Inside, panic was beginning to rage. All the while the reflection had a smirk that grew wider and wider until it began to laugh. An uncontrollable laugh. What he felt and what he saw were not the same thing. He was no longer behind the wheel; he was behind the eyes. Trapped.

'Hello, Father.'

It was *him*. How could it be?

The voice spoke again; true and proud with a hint of mockery. 'It is I. The authentic hobgoblin, the ginger with no head.'

Finbarr tried to speak but his words just bounced about his head like a peanut in a jar. He tried to move but his legs were two spades stuck in clay. All the while, the eyes of his son glared deeply into the leftovers of Finbarr's soul.

The weeks and months went by, and not one could go anywhere without the other. A bond no father and son had ever had before. Ginger had the say on walking, talking and pretty much the whole shebang; Finbarr, incarcerated within the mind of his son. Existing, that was all – a truly voiceless Irishman.

Finbarr now spent his days in resentment at his son's way of life. Ginger spend most of it wasting time at work instead of being at the pub. Probably for the best. It keeps him from having to endure Ginger's choice of drink; gin and tonic. Finbarr still had his own thoughts, he just had to make sure his son was busy when he indulged in them. He spent every conscious moment trying to devise a plan to gain control for himself. Could he think so hard it would push Ginger back to wherever he was before? Could he embarrass Ginger so much that he would never want to show his face again, leaving him to take charge? It all started to seem futile and giving up looked like his only option.

Then one day, when all was looking bleak, Ginger was perched on a wall at the edge of Queen's Bridge. He tumbled backwards, hitting his head. Soon after, Finbarr realised he had a feeling. Like his whole body was recovering from paraesthesia. He had control. He thought about going to the pub at first; oh, how he would have killed for a Guinness. Instead, he thought a little longer. He peered over the edge of the bridge and down to the river that flowed beneath. It was as surreal as anything he ever saw with his own eyes. As his son began to wake, he looked down once again and knew just what to do.

It was simple; a voiceless Irishman is no Irishman at all.

P. J. Hale

A Thousand Wolves Have Eaten Grandmother

The Author has been arrested for crimes against conventional story-telling.

The trial begins with this announcement. It is made to a room filled with the echoes of heavy and precise words like 'allegation' and 'objection'. The announcement is followed by a brief but intense silence.

(Someone laughs, probably The Author.)

We are here to talk about stories, the speaker goes on to explain. As we all know, stories have a definite shape: a beginning, a middle, an end.

The speaker waves his hands to emphasise his words, creating an unrecognisable shape in the air.

(A picture paints a thousand words, someone else adds, and is ignored.)

Explain to me exactly what the problem is, The Author says, standing up and surveying the room with the air of a person who plans to write this all down for future use. The Author is eating a cheese and tomato sandwich and speaks between bites.

Another lengthy silence follows The Author's words. This time, the silence crackles like static.

We have evidence, the speaker continues, punctuating his words with the tapping of a determined finger on the table in front of him. There is a flurry of movement and a book is retrieved from where it has been strategically stashed at the edge of the room. It is slammed onto the table.

Fairy tales, the book-slammer says dramatically. Exhibit A. Fairy tales.

Ah, says The Author, breathing in deeply to inhale the musty scent of the yellowed pages.

It's all here, the book-slammer continues. Everything you need to know about stories. It's quite simple really –

– It's not that simple.

– It's very simple. A thousand witches have been slain; a thousand servant-girls have gone to the ball; a thousand wolves have devoured an unsuspecting grandmother.

The Author sits back down. Who's been eating my sandwich?

You simply have to write stories as they are supposed to be written. Follow the rules. Construct a plausible sequence of events and tie everything up at the end in a neat, little parcel with a neat, little bow.

The proceedings are interrupted by a loud, rumbling noise, one that sounds very much like a thousand writers have been let into the building. From what they can hear, members of the angry mob are yelling at one another about punctuation (apostrophe *after* the 's', you fool!) and debating whether the world creates language or language creates the world.

With the exception of The Author, everyone in the room starts to look very nervous.

How many cases did we have booked in for today? someone asks.

Umm, three? comes the anxious reply. I think it was supposed to be three...

Will someone please find out what's going on?

As the commotion continues, The Author takes a moment to think, brushing sandwich crumbs from the table onto the floor. The Author considers sneaking out through a side door or climbing out of a window.

Instead of moving, The Author looks towards the court stenographer who is writing down everything that is being said during the trial.

I hope that's helpful, whatever you're writing, The Author says. Will I get a copy?

No response.

Is the stenographer allowed to speak? The Author wonders. Or is she reluctant to? She would be forced to transcribe her own words.

The harried movements in the room have ceased. In the background, the sounds of the angry mob can still be heard. The Author hopes that the trial will be over soon. The Author hopes that the narrow-minded, traditional-thinking court will be obliterated by the angry mob of writers.

Someone clears their throat and says,

This trial is about writing.

(Writing is a trial, The Author mumbles.)

Emily Hambley

Unverisimilitudinous

Four years in is when the man behind the glass changes. Long after you'd changed, long after you'd given up on believing that it was a matter of perception that would settle in due time. It happens on the dusky, achromatic morning of a nation on the tipping point. You enter your small damp-smelling bathroom to scrub off the sleep and the overnight crust that clings to your skin. Afterwards, you lift your head to gaze into your square mirror, half-fogged, above the sink. The man is there, as he always is, playing mimic to your every gesture with a rugged flare that sinks hooks through your diaphragm, as he always does. You wipe your face dry. You stare at him. And he blinks.

You don't think anything of it for the initial ten seconds. It's early. You're groggy, and your head's not been in the most reliable place for the past few weeks. You're a paranoid before you're a person at the best of times, so you dismiss it as a muddled misperception as you lift your hand to the mirror at the same time, just to be sure.

The man raises no such hand. His face gazes out to you dully, nigh-unrecognisable in its ruggedness. You find yourself staring in mute transfixion, feeling the way that your heart, tongue, and throat meld into a single continuous pulsing stretch of flesh inside your body. You take a step back, barely feeling the way your bare foot squelches through a lukewarm splash puddle.

He, still looking at you, clears his throat. You feel it in your own throat, a clogging rumble that stretches your vocal chords into a long disused position. You have to swallow thrice before the sensation of strangulation abates. He looks on at you with a stilled patience as you gather yourself. Then he says you look spooked. The voice reverberates in that part of your mind that tricks your hypnagogic subconscious into hearing deafening screams, that turns silence into volume. It glides over your mind, hitting notes that you know, yet do not.

That first time, you don't reply. You make an animalistic, guttural stutter, then spin and scramble out of the bathroom before you can scream. You're half asleep, you say to yourself as you dress in your bedroom, door barricaded by your desk chair. It's a waking dream. Nothing happened.

Still, you quickly stop looking into the mirror, and whatever might inhabit that uncertain space of reflection. Just in case you really did see something wrong. Just in case it looks back.

*

You were right to. Encounter number two takes place the next time you set foot in the bathroom, two days later. Still hungover from a post-election misery binge, you head to the bathroom in search of reprieve from that terrible parliament livestream blaring from your phone. As you wait for the electric bulb to flicker to full strength, you glance over at the mirror.

The man is still there, standing behind the condensation stains with a flatly curious expression. You want to look away from him, but you cannot.

He tilts his head to the side a little, like an owl. He says what's your problem. Asks if you really can't handle a bit of news. Says you would've celebrated that, once upon a time. You would have celebrated before.

You clench one fist and breathe around a dry throat. The overwhelming urge to swing at the glass, to break, to destroy, to feel angry, seeps through your skin like viral droplets. You blink back tears. You do not feel rage. You cannot. Not any more.

He says come on, get pissed off.

This is not real, you tell yourself. But only in your head. Only where it doesn't matter.

*

You stop using the upstairs bathroom after that. Every morning and evening, you bring yourself to the downstairs en suite, where the muted cream colour scheme succeeds in soothing, where the glass doesn't harm you, where you can breathe.

It becomes routine. Wake go down check the news cycle wash go out come back check the news cycle wash go up sleep avoid the upstairs room avoid the upstairs room avoid the upstairs room. You mystify it, let it grow into a grim Other that looms above your head, tendril fingers seeping through the fabric of your walls and scraping the back of your neck like a cold whisper. You make it powerful.

Four weeks drift by in relative calm before instance number three. You exist in a comfortable miasma, the madwoman who never washes upstairs, going a little batty from living alone, but that's okay. Until it stops being so, in the new year and new decade, on a day where your mother comes over to stay and the news is dominated by talks of galvanising the ugliest parts of international foreign policies.

She takes the downstairs en suite. You have no room to object. She kisses your cheek, overwhelms you with her perfume. Says how beautiful you're becoming, as if daily pills constitute beauty. You thank her anyway. This is how she makes her effort.

You don't talk politics. She sees and hears what fills you with slow-rotting terror and feels a warm rush of relieved pleasure, a fat cat gloating in the victory of the mangled bird in its jaws. You spend the evening watching her soaps with her, then force yourself upstairs for your nightly routine.

He says you're an over-reactor, as you slip through the door bathed in a clammy sweat. Says you're delusional.

Your mother snores downstairs. It gives you the bravado to speak. You say shut up. He shouldn't exist.

He says man up. Scratches at his stubble and scoffs. Glares at you, like a looming magnifying glass honing in on a lone ant.

You force yourself to meet his gaze right back. Ask why he's doing this.

He asks why *you're* doing this. Why you tell yourself *he* and *you* are distinct entities. Why you killed him. Why you made this mistake. It's suicide, you know. Should've stuck with the life you threw out.

He frowns, shakes his head, laughs, on and on and on. Like he knows you. Like he's won. You're seized by a glimpse of a future where he persists in this cruel stasis, and with a damp creak across the surface of your brain, realise that you can't stand having this shade leeching off you for a single moment longer. You have changed. He has not. That realisation alone shrinks him to nothing.

You punch the mirror. The glass crunches under your skin, stabs into your knuckles, leaves smudged blood streaks across its surface. Everything falls silent. Nursing your mangled hand, you begin to weep.

*

At the end of the month, on a day of international transition into new and dangerous waters, you finally replace the bathroom mirror. This new one is perfectly circular and catches the sun in a way that lights up the whole room.

When you look into the reflection, for the first time you only see, and will always only see, yourself.

Conor Hannon

Desiccare

Returned,
it comes back to me.

Money. Small victories. Hand on shoulder.

Back home in the shadow
of the second largest tulip tree in Massachusetts,
your house, now stripped bare, for sale.
Punchdrunk with absence, its slump-hipped roof.
Its ivy, a negligee of neglect.
Outliving time and purpose
its deeper, hidden bruise.

After an unprecedented summer of drought
late season heat portends a reckoning.
In driest soil, a lessened bounty.
The diminished reach of roots.

Like others to come, this New England autumn
will release itself too early.
Fewer trees will flare burnt red, sienna, ochre.
Fewer leaves – five-fingered fires – will promise
the cycle complete.

Yet,
boughs overwrought and out of sync still know how to let go.
They drop
leaf
after
loved leaf   edges
           curled
           and
           brown.

(cont.)

Like the card returned with your name through my letterbox.
Sealed still,
a bud of unbroken
two-lipped sorrow,
my last whisper to you.

> *There is more here for you,*
> *it lied.*

Leaves, lattice-laced, desiccate with death
still provide the necessary metaphor.
Ready for burning, they will catch
the last rasp of September's air.
They will restore the rubied light of a million dead suns
in each their turning,
in each their fall.

S.L. Holm

Warpaint

Social relations are changing, and your make-up should change with them. Our new range of emotional cosmetics may be just the weapon you need. Each product releases nanomemes into your bloodstream to alter your mood accordingly, and is guaranteed to juice you up with the emotions you need to do battle.

Our range includes:

= Angry Lipstick. Everyone knows that words can hurt far more than sticks and stones. Give your words their maximum effect by adding anger to your mouth. Our various shades of ire will soak into your lips and fill your bloodstream with the memes you need to do battle. Choose from a light pink irritation to a luscious purple rage, and turn those pouting, kissable lips into a deadly weapon.

= Thick Skin Foundation. Applied liberally to the face, this foundation contains nanomemes that will protect you from any kind of insult or barb that your opponent may care to make. The foundation will cloak your mind with a shield of insensitivity, meaning you won't take these ill-meant comments to heart. You'll be able to dish out the verbal onslaught – but won't have to suffer from it in return.

= Touchy Nails. This varnish works in the opposite way to our foundation – it will harden your nails, but soften your defences, so you become more sensitive to the hidden meanings of other people's banter. If you've ever wondered if something was meant as an insult, use this nail varnish and you'll be certain. You can choose your shade to suit the level of overthinking required.

= Shadow Eyes. The eyes are the windows to the soul, and our eye shadow will darken your soul along with your eyes. Any thoughts of empathy or humanity will dissolve, turning you away from the light and into the dark night of the soul. We advise you to use it sparingly; just as subtlety is the key to a fascinating face, a light touch is the key to becoming less forgiving and more brooding.

= Involvement Mascara. Don't let firm boundaries spoil your battle. Touch up your lashes with this mascara, and feel the warm glow of righteousness as it slowly becomes all about you. As the nanomemes reach your cerebral cortex, you will stop worrying about whether this is someone else's argument or whether you should stay out of it. This makes it an ideal cosmetic to put on just before a bout of social media.

= Memory Rouge. To forgive is to forget, so make sure you remember by rubbing some of our mnemonic colour into your cheeks. These nanomemes will search your brain for slights and grudges from childhood and even earlier. You'll discover wrongs that you had completely forgotten, and will offer up the retaliation that was always due. Don't let bygones be bygones – put the past at the forefront of your attack.

= Concealer. Never mind blemishes in your face – this concealer works on your mind. Once absorbed, it works on those thoughts that might diminish your attack – feelings of guilt, or sympathy for the other's point of view. You will stay focussed on the rightness of your cause, and you won't be distracted by doubts that your enemy could use against you. Just a few dabs, and you'll never pull a punch again!

Emotional cosmetics are for novelty use only and under strict supervision. Not suitable for under-18s. Couples with relationship problems are advised to seek counselling.

Neil James Hudson

ContactLess

Letter, Rip, Peel.
Private and Confidential, Banking made easier.
Rectangle, Thin, Plastic.
Fits perfectly into its delegated slot.
Insert, Pin, Cash.
Crisp polymer sheets, released with worth only in trade.

Food – *Tap*
Clothes – *Tap*
Phone – *Tap*

Balance, £0.00, Job?
Enclosed is your financial statement.
Work, Save, Spend. Continuous motion of a rotating wheel.

Today, Tomorrow, Always.
Forever trying to save only to waste on the material.

Friendship – *Tap*
Family – *Tap*
Happiness – *Declined*

Tap Tap Tap.

Sarah Ikin

Your Love Letters Must Have Gotten Lost

Dear Humanity,
             The red stains from your fistfuls of kisses
are the bruises that remain, unfading in my cheeks.
Plastered and painted by foundations, constructions,
cities, skyscrapers, sewers. Factories. Landfill.

Cavernous scars: stretchmarks. As my skin changes, ages, grows
like yours. They bow and arch like your
precious ribs. Still, your penetrations, drills, mining operations
are no longer surgical. They discard, thrive on your disregard, that I
    am living.

My stomach whipped up a concoction: wind, no rain
and flames. That acid prickles, sputtering across my skin.
Why do burning bushes, with cause and risk and pain,
mean sceptics, remain oblivious? Free to look a different way…

Your next stage of evolution is
evasion? ~~Hiding~~ Running from a dispersing truth.
Allergens are on the rise; the skies are choking with you.
Runny nose, dry throat, sticky eyes

as my open lungs are corrupted by your emissions.
Your omissions – silence – as trees collapse,
chewed through, falling in forests
to be heard by hundreds of deaf ears.

                    With Love,
                         The Only Planet Earth

                                   Emily Jayne

Paper Grenade

Bundled into a wooden chest for what seemed like centuries. In truth, it was only a decade. Kneeling there, I stare at the fading leather-bound diary laying on top of grandad's old soldier uniform. Picking up the diary I begin to examine it for the hundredth time, tracing my finger over the cracks of the blinding.

Someone once told me a diary is a friend you can carry around; doesn't talk or argue back. Most of all the temptation to confide all your worries, woes and wishes for the future. So, did he write the diary to be read? Do the dead even care for privacy?

I hold up the diary higher to my nose and hope that it still smells of him. Instead, my nostrils are filled with dust, causing me to choke. Recovering, I make my way over to the desk and plonk myself on my chair that has the most elegant ornate cabriole legs. Flicking the desk light on, I sit and ponder over the decision to read what tales are told within the pages. Is this a violation of privacy? Or a tribute to his memory? The window into his inner thoughts. I feel myself getting more questions rather than answers.

I flip through the dog-eared pages as if there were something that would set itself free. I was half expecting it to be cryptic, but there is no secret language to translate. No symbols to decipher, no Morse code. Just the scrawny writing of the era and once crisp white pages now stained by life.

After, returning, Grandad stuffed the diary under his and nanna's mattress. There it lay throughout Grandad's illnesses, nightmares and the conception of my father. If it could speak it would seriously complain.

'Hide it, keep it safe.' The instructions he left on his death bed. I've respected his wishes all these years. I hid it in this wooden chest, letting it lay dormant, fearing if I disobeyed his instructions a Pandora box scenario… I shiver at the thought.

When I was young, he would tell me stories of his time in the war. The mischief he and the Belgian students got up to and the tricks they played on the nuns. Then his time in the trenches making it sound like he fought the jerries single handed. Even about that soldier! So, whatever he wanted me to know in life he told me himself. Wouldn't he?

During a project of World War I at school, I discovered diaries in wartime were generally forbidden with the danger of it falling into enemy hands, but Grandad was never one for rules.

It's frightening, how this was once growing in a forest surrounded by woodland creatures doing their business. Add a little leather and binding, now it's the most manipulative and chilling object I've ever come across. And these days the kids have Social Media.

What would you do for others not to read your long-buried secrets?

It cannot speak, but long buried secrets are about to explode. For this diary is a paper grenade.

Sophie Kilmartin

Boxes

Alison wants to sell me boxes. She emails me
every day at 09.14 then follows-up on Twitter.
We're on #firstnameterms but we've never met.
Alison chats to me about boxes like a pal might
ask about your weekend. They are *well durable*,
she says. Some are even *tamper evident. You
haven't even seen polypropylene until you've seen
our polypropylene. Hurry, there are now only [273]
in stock.* From what I see, they come in

> sputum green
> slag-heap grey
> or chicken-heart yellow.

On screen they hang suspended – dangling pixels
of tupperworld competing for best light. If you
hover over one, it spins to show every side, but
every side is exactly the same. I have no idea
why Alison believes I need boxes or what she
thinks I would do with them. *I'm not even sure
she is who she says she is.* One day, I wake up with
#darkfeelings about Alison and her boxes. In a
slow fluster, I attempt to instantly unsubscribe,
but I am quickly taken to a page that reads: *did
you really mean to instantly unsubscribe?* This
makes me carefully consider if I really mean to
instantly unsubscribe.

I click no.

Now I'm back to emails from Alison who wants
to sell me boxes. But we have a new relationship
based on better understanding. She knows that
I will never buy a box from her, no matter how
durable or shiny it is. And I know that she will

email me every day at 09.14 with the latest offer on box sales – regardless of warfare, government collapse or global pandemic. Alison has become the #boxbuddy I didn't know I needed. I look forward to her emails and I think she is pleased to be sending them to me. No boxes will ever be bought or sold as an outcome of this e-dalliance but sometimes it's just nice to connect with someone else in an ill-matched but well-boxed part of the universe.

Nicky Kippax

#GE2019

Sadness at the trailing colours
Crimson soppy, snowflake socialist
All I see is red
When all there is, is blue, sadness, depression
Melancholy high school English literature teacher's metaphor
To keep you in mind
Of empathy, of the meaning of it all
Of what it all means?
I'm not sure anymore

One thing is for sure,
Whether I wake up tomorrow with skies of blue and roses red in hue
Or of gloomy dishevelled pictures of the past of me and you
I will be thankful
For me
And for you
For us

For this planet too
For having the right to fight
To fight back
To fight for
To fight to
Towards futures with us all

Because
There is no human mass extinction here
We did that to all the other species
Perhaps they're safe now, in history
Our toxic touch cast-carbon dated
As a permanent singleton, left for dust

(cont.)

But we are left to deal with what we have done
But we are divided with what we have done
But all we want is to love those we love, right?

So be it?
Just bitterness blizzards fogging the lens on a crisp winter's day
Or that the other half have lost that metaphor
The depth of penetrating aquamarine flowing through our veins?

Remember the importance
To love those around you
In every breath you say

Hold on tight,
We survive this way

R. E. Kirby

Clouds at Sunset

The clouds that float above me, soft and white / against the sky of changing hue, at points / and peaks seem like pure white snow, firm and crisp / enough for me to eat in scoops. If I / reached out from up atop that tree, whose branches / knot and coil above its trunk, and leaves / which dance on edge with air and sky, horizon / high, I dare say I could clutch these clouds, / and bring them with me to the ground, to rest / on them when evening settles down. Upon / first glance the clouds seemed flat, but now I've crossed / some unclear line of condensed rain they / solidify. Clouds made of rain that used to lie / on earth, but rose above, to fall to earth / but rise above. A cycle never ending; / a cycle that refused to die despite, / the droughts and waves of heat, the rain soon came / back down again to us mere mortals, cold / and plain, ungrateful for the summer sun, / yet yearning for it when it's gone. The sun / which separates this sky, and approaches / its western side, casts warmth and light to poke / between a gap in grey-ish clouds that mark / the rain, like pin pricks burning hot and white / as darkness chases sun to night. Over / man-shaped hills of earthen make they are / pursued by sunset air, that dusk enlightens / with its flair, in blushed pinks and orange / rays; dusk pushes blue and white of clouds / that rest within retreating sky, as sun's / light bursts the clouded edge, and cracks it down / the middle from its companion, resting / just behind, like bolts of lightning from / the gods of old. It cuts these clouds from one / another, so they may no more embrace / each other.

I sit, as lazy as a stone / watching clouds, in the backseat / of a car driving human roads, / layered over nature's home, / wishing clouds were crisp yet soft, / but not quite as cold as snow.

Adam Kirkbride

No. 85 to Hull Interchange

I'm sat on this bumbling bus and it's late.
Some kid in trackies is kicking my chair
it smells like piss
we're all pissed.

A frail old bird of a lady catches me unaware,
'What's the time?'
'Sorry what?'
I take out an earphone
'Hang on... what?'
'What time is it, love?'
the watch on her wrist catches the light but-
I fumble with my phone
'Oh – it's two o'clock.'

Later she shuffles to the seat next to me,
'The sun was in my eyes.'
I smile, 'Ah.'
I don't care much about the sun
when a grizzly toddler starts to roar

'How old are you, love?'
'How old am I?' I sound thick
she nods, the elderly sure talk a lot
'I'm seventeen.'
'Oh, I remember being seventeen.'
Oh God. Please don't.

She spares me an anecdote
but fires another question,
'How old do I look?'
she wears metal glasses which settle in deep grooves of wrinkles,
why is she asking me?

'I couldn't say' I splutter,
she looks *old,*
the jasmine perfume practically falls off her in waves
and muddles with the musk of the old bus
'I don't know... I can't say'

She smiles with yellow teeth
'Don't worry about me, love'
I smile in return and plead with my eyes
forgive me
but right now, talking to people makes my skin feel like static.
My hand brushes the chalky velvet of my seat
and I cringe.

She moves then, to the front of the bus
and starts talking
again
to another stranger.
And I wonder if we,
daydreaming
transient
awkward teenagers
on stinking buses
are all she's got.

Laura Kirkwood

A summit made of moulded darkness

yesterday, I was cold, I pushed myself into the corner of my bedroom
and hid from the world outside, the trees, the branches, the leaves,
the landscape of the soil and where the soil meets the pavement.

the universe is decaying against a nation of greedy creatures,
and I am a microcosm fighting a complex nature of cognitions,
the lights are no longer lit, I am no longer just cold,
I have become scared, shadows are now my companions,
I can hear the earth turning and I am climbing mountains that no
    longer stand straight,
cliffs that are crumbling back to the ground they once emerged from.

I am floating in a sea full of plastic memories, the waves gaining
    strength and
opposing my fragile frame, the currents knock me back and
I am in bed, cradled in covers, and yet,
I am still cold.

Amy Langton

The Self-Contradictory Nature of Cameron Law

He is crass but also tame.

Take that one time he was at a pub with a few people. He wouldn't call them mates, he didn't know them that well and wasn't comfortable sharing intimate details about himself. To him, this evening felt more like a business trip than a social outing: He was networking, adding social media contacts and taking in their faces so he could turn to them for group projects. He hadn't spoken for 4 minutes, he knew that, he was making a mental note of it. He realises that he can't let this audition of his go to waste, his mind whirls, thinking of what worked in previous situations.

'Knock, knock.'

'Who's there?'

'Not Madeline McCann.'

That caused an uproar at home. Maybe he should try that?

He decided it was too risky and took a big gulp of cider instead.

He cries hard but dances harder.

Cameron drowns his pillow.

'That was stupid lol,' he thinks to himself.

He's now dancing to ABBA.

He wants to push himself but keeps pulling himself back.

How to feel like a piece of shit in four simple steps:

1. Think about creating something. This could be anything that pops into your head. It doesn't matter if you haven't done it before, that's part of the learning process!

2. Don't actually create anything. Alternatively, make a start of something, get frustrated because it wasn't perfect the first time and give up.

3. Beat yourself up about it! That's all you're good at!

4. Simply rinse and repeat!

He wants to be single but also wants to be in a relationship.

'Why did you date her? You're way too good for her!'

'Why did you get with her? You can do better than that.'

Cameron has heard these comments a lot lately.

Three thoughts have emerged from said comments.

Firstly, it was kind of harsh on the girls that had chosen to be intimate with Cameron. Okay he's not a white knight. He'll admit that some of them were mistakes formed from a combination of desperation and alcohol, but for the majority, he still thinks fondly of. He was grateful that they chose to give him a chance, especially given that he isn't much of a looker, as, on a good day, he might just qualify as a seven. Hell, some of them even made the first move which he found both extremely attractive and progressive.

Secondly, was the latter comment a compliment or an insult? Cameron likes to believe that it's a compliment because it's usually his friends who are saying it. What if Cameron genuinely liked that girl because they had an interesting discussion? Not simply because of physical appearance? What if they're actually mocking him and laughing at him, the moment he turns his back?

No. He doesn't want to think like that anymore.

Finally, what does it say about Cameron as a person? Does he go for the 'low-hanging fruit' simply because it's the only option? Maybe because it requires less effort-?

Cameron has been single for quite a while now; he doesn't really know how to feel about it. Originally, it was like letting go of a 50kg weight. He could finally do what he wanted, where he wanted, when he wanted. He didn't have to worry about those little things he had to do to make sure his partner was content; the daily texts, the buying of gifts and constantly saying 'yes' and 'sorry' to her. It all went up in smoke, the ball and chain he didn't even realise was there had been unshackled. He reconnected with friends, put more focus into his university work and played a bunch of sweet, sweet videogames. He had saved a lot of money from being single, he could treat himself to a bit of relaxation every now and then and he was up to play anything! A game where you play as a goose who terrorizes a British village in a minimalist art style, has menus like British motorway signs and a designated 'honk button'? Hell yeah! Sign him up!

However, as much as he loves having all of these new experiences, he has no one to share them with. It seems like some things are just naturally better in twos. There were some co-op games that caught Cameron's eye, but he knew that they were practically unplayable with an AI companion. His family never really saw the appeal of video games, so he couldn't play with them, and, being at a university 200 miles away from home didn't help. And while some his friends enjoyed video games, they played different consoles and stuck to their online competitive multiplayer games, which aren't really Cameron's cup of tea. So, for the majority of the time, Cameron's experiences and passions belonged solely to himself. He wanted someone to share experiences and passions with, so they would constantly pass their interests back and forth.

Something like this...

'Okay, tonight we can watch a few episodes of [insert TV show they love here] then a few levels of Overcooked after that. Sound good to you?'

'Oh yes, that sounds great! Oh, Cameron you're so handsome and strong and humble and creative and witty and acne-free!'

As great as this all sounds, Cameron wonders how much he would have to sacrifice to get to that stage...? First and most difficult, there's getting someone's attention. Then there's the expenses. Dating can get expensive when some girls expect you to pay for everything. Then getting comfortable enough to open up to someone so freely like that... that's going to take a while. Finally, and most impactful of all, he simply doesn't have the time. He's in his final year of university, make or break time. It also means he'd be heading home soon and hopefully travelling abroad and Cameron learnt the hard way that long distance relationships simply don't work. He puts a record on.

'Someday I'll find her
And I'm still reminded
Maybe she's best in dreams' – 'Dreamin', Mac DeMarco

Cameron Law

Changes

Can you leave your hat on?
And watch me.
Don't get comfortable,
You can't sit down, but you can lie.
You can taunt and talk about,
Change…

Leave your hat on,
I'm not finished.
Don't get comfortable.
You watched,
Stripping, fabrics of velvet slipping from her chest,
You touched,
'Leave your hat on sweetheart'
You've done this to yourself.
You can't rest it here anymore…
Not when you've rested it somewhere else.

Kerri-Anne Lee

Maths

My thirty-year-old daughter started speaking
in gender-neutral pronouns
out of the blue, and I
(because I'm 50?)
fundamentally – you might say embarrassingly – misunderstood.
My daughter told me that 'Marlene' had done her a 'month-long
favour' by looking after the dog, and so my daughter bought a
thank-you gift. My daughter said

'I bought them a bike.'

I add all this up – the 'Marlene' and the 'them' – and work out that
'Marlene is from a couple'
and then, out loud, in all sincerity, I say
'So will they share the bike? Or is it a tandem?'

And I get this look,
which is all about my sleepy [northern] lack of *woke* (my daughter
can be like that sometimes).
But I accept it. Totally.
And while I don't immediately adopt or adapt to this singular version
of 'they' or 'them,' it penetrates.
I find I care

to improve.

A day later, I'm on the metro when a very beautiful human indeed
gets on.
So exquisite that (truthfully I do this a lot)
I take a surreptitious photo, just in case my mental pen portrait fails
me later:
precision-placed beanie of the softest cashmere in the palest blue,
choppy, charcoal bob, angled in perfect parallel with the jawline,
delicate chin, dipped towards a phone, emphasising symmetry by drawing
    attention to

the angle of that geometric nose
and exposing the full extent of those almond-eyelids
powdered in vivid purple, and blacklined with a scrupulously carefree
  flick…

I observe myself, mentally adding and subtracting *all the data*
  — trying to calculate at least some of
  — the sum of this
     being.
The hair, the eyes, the demure twist of the long limbs, the skinny,
  braceletted ankle = **girl**
(plus or minus) *the leg-hair, the flat chest, the shoe-size* = **boy.**

But don't get *me* wrong.

However it may look,
(just because I'm 50?!)
I understand that I am really just observing floating abstractions
coming and going and messing me about, as they've always done,
trying to *make* a thing, so that I *know* the thing.

And I might be from those simple arithmetical days
where someone who looked like this *vision* equated to
'neither nowt nor summat'
but I always hated maths.

Thank you Universe, I think to myself, right there and then on the
  metro.
First for sending me this timely, practical and gorgeous application
  for the 'they' or 'them'
I may or may not choose to use (for now at least).
And second, for a reminder of the natural bend of the wondering
  brain;
the ultimate body-elastic,
our *liberally-plastic-fantastic.*

Marcia Mackey

Dollhouse

Dollhouse.
What does it mean?
To me…
It means something like a wooden facade of life.
Life can seem so; performance ready,
So rehearsed
until you trip up.
And the tears start falling.

The tears wipe away that mask.
The one you worked so hard creating
Protecting yourself like a wall,
Stood tall to keep everyone and anyone out
who may hurt you.

This time is different.
This time, people are there to help you,
pick yourself up.
They are that tall tree you needed,
to prop yourself upon.

The frame you needed to prove your shine.
You will Shine as bright as the star
You once were.
Leave the Dollhouse
and shine brightly.

A. B. Maloney

In Their Eyes

Beleaguered eyes look down at the stern
Its wake syphoning through melted synthetics,
From hurried hands that have touched and tossed
And disregarded.
    The roughness in their eyes,
     A pillar of satisfaction, as they look on
     At dazzling screens, with impeccable lights.

       From the sources,
         to the tributaries,
            I drift delicately through,
              These foreign surroundings.
       Emeralds and azures and,
         Beating wildlife
           Pumping a puff of methane, slowly
           Into the air.

Scathing eyes gather,
In mass crowds of banquets
Where those in tip-top shoes,
Comb back their ill-fated hair
And smile and laugh
As time, continues to pass.
       Forgetting this forsaken plastic.
      The absence of ignorance,
       and no flippant *ok's*
        to me and I.
        And instead,
        O   O
      Pick up that bottle please.

Andrew Milne

House-hunting

The year is 2006. David Tennant is Doctor Who, *Dick and Dom in Da Bungalow* is in its final season, and my brother Harry and I are waiting to be picked up by our dad, so that we could stay with him for the weekend. Bags packed with clothes, we would sit outside on the porch, until we spotted our Dad rounding the corner; and then we'd quickly say goodbye to our Mother, and rush over to meet him. I had learned over time that I had to be ready to go with my shoes on before Dad came for us, otherwise Mum would be irritated that she would have to face her ex-husband for longer than she had previously anticipated.

I often wondered why it had to be this way. Why don't they get along? I would think. They're my parents, they're supposed to get along! Nearly every weekend it was the same. Dad would arrive and Mum would make small talk with him at the door as Harry and I collected any last-minute things. It was, as I would find out in later life, a rather awkward affair for my Dad. Things were difficult between Sally and himself ever since the breakup, he was living in a cold flat with not a lot of money to live on, yet she was living in a nice house and seemingly couldn't be happier. All the while, the government was telling him that he had to pay child support to keep seeing the two of us. It was a hard time, a sad time that he struggled to pull through. But, as Harry and I were too young to understand what was going on, it seemed very normal to us.

At the time, my dad, Evan, lived in a small flat on the other side of town. He resided in flat ten on the fourth floor, which to a seven-year-old who was in desperate need of a growth spurt, felt like climbing Everest. Harry, however, never seemed to be bothered by the stairs – or as time went by – any steep structures at all, which is a trait that baffles me to this day.

Harry is like a mountain goat. On one occasion, the three of us were climbing the Welsh Mount Mwnt, Dad and myself struggled to get up due to stiff legs and a shared fear of falling back down again, whereas Harry was already halfway up. By the time Dad and I had arrived at the top, my brother was sitting on the peak, and said: 'what took you so long? I've been here for ten minutes.' This is an ability that I have always been jealous of.

After braving Mount Staircase, the flat would become a welcome sight. Sadly, upon further investigation, the flat most likely was not the best location to live, due to the amount of problems it had. Namely, the worst being the lack of any heating whatsoever, or the fact that there was only one bed. The problem with the bed was the biggest one. To get around this, my brother and I would have to take it in turns each night to sleep in the bed with Dad. The other would sleep on a portable bed on the floor. However, the sleeping arrangements often ended up with both my brother and I sleeping in the bed, and our father on the floor.

It wasn't the best, but it was a step up, and still warmer than our Dad's previous lodgings; located over a block of shops on the high street. This previous flat was very cold and had walls like paper. But of course, having no money, he had no way of improving it. He said that it was an improvement from sleeping on his friends' floor, as he had in the first few months after the breakup; but seeing how cold the flat was, I wondered if he was saying that for our benefit, or his own.

The idea of living above the high street was very interesting to me. Before Dad read us our bedtime story, I liked looking out of the window and watching the busy people wander under the amber glowing lights, imagining what had brought them to this area in the first place.

When our dad couldn't see us for the weekend, we stayed with our grandparents on our mother's side. They were nice enough people; Grandma would make biscuits and other treats with us every time we visited. I always loved that, but I never really liked staying overnight. My grandparent's old house looked very scary at night, and I always ended up falling asleep while hiding under the covers from monsters that would emerge from the shadows of the dark house, taking their victims away from their beds to eat for their supper. For that reason, I always preferred staying with Dad, because I knew that I wasn't alone.

It was tough for him to be in that situation, but I knew that he always looked forward to seeing me and Harry the most, because no matter how hard things were, we would treat life as an adventure. He needed us, and we needed him too.

Life at Mum's house could at best be described as tense. At this point, Mum's at-the-time fiancée, Kev, had lived with us for about two years now. In the right mood, Kev could be nice. However, one small nudge in the wrong direction could set him to erupt more than a volcano, so Harry and I had to be careful of what we said, lest we face his wrath. I looked forward to seeing Dad on the weekends the most, because that meant a short respite where I could relax and focus only on having fun with my father and brother.

When Dad had saved enough money for a deposit, he began to look for a house. He had told us about this, and we were very much looking forward to it. A warm house, with our own rooms, with our own mess; where when we left to go back to our mother's house, we could come back and have things exactly the same as when we had left it. No more packing clothes, we would have our own chest of drawers for that. It would be somewhere we could feel safe.

Eventually, Dad found a house that when we went to view it, we thought was perfect. It was a small house, with a living room, a very small kitchen and an even smaller bathroom. It had its problems, like the weeds in the garden, the noisy dog next door, and the damp walls in my room, but we loved it. And it was only half an hour's walk from Mum's house.

As soon as we could, we bought the house and moved in, quickly making more friends nearby than I could count. The three of us have been happy living there ever since.

Jeremy Ceri Mitchell

The Clouds

I find myself focusing on the clouds.
Not the smog blocking my eyes.
Not the deafening canons bursting my ears.
Not the men I've watched die.

Wishing the fighting was more detached.
Not so dirty.
Not so visceral.
Not so agonising.

Watching a man's life leave his eyes.
I feel the weight of guilt.
I feel the thrum of battle.
I feel the need to push through.

I hope for sons of sons to experience war differently.
For this war will end.
Another war will begin.
I can only pray for war to change.

* * *

I find myself focusing on the clouds.
Not the people.
Not the weapons.
Not what I should be doing.

Looking through the eyes in the sky,
I stare at life from afar.
I stare at death from my office chair.
I stare at history through a screen.

Across the oceans and mountains and cities.
I hope to see nothing.
I hope to see everything.
I hope for it to end.

The actions of this drone control my future.
My country's future.
The world's future.
But the future is already here.

Lucy Morton

Phone Assessment

my voice is too carried on the breeze
but   too loud   into the receiver
and for some reason,
is saying all the things I never say
                              so often they feel sometimes like stories

and I feel keenly   my fraudulent mis-stepping
in the sunlit middle of a work day
feeling ok today but not usually   usually feeling ok

and saying the words without the feeling
is not the same as saying words without feeling the way my voice does

when I am feeling that way

I feel the ground unevening my steps

and the voice through the speaker tells me   it is sorry and I tell it
not to worry
it's not that I want to

        it's that I feel like I might   get to wanting to

and that wanting to might make me not want to anymore

or want   to cleave my head into quarters
though practically I couldn't make it past halves

Laura Newberry

It's not quite right

It's not quite right when I look outside
To see the world so very horrified
Yet I don't understand – how is this justified?
When the problems can be so easily identified.

It's not quite right when I go out at night
And watch two grown men throw fists with all their might
Because a girl crying down by my right
Tried to put up a fight.

It's not quite right when I hear of a boy who dared be free
And I want to shout out and agree
It is our human right to be in love with whoever we want to be!
But I can't because of who might hear me.

It's not quite right when girls want to be boys
And their parents say, "it's just a phase, go play with your toys,"
And they wonder if they will ever find joy
Spending their whole life living as a decoy.

It's not quite right when we blame the victim
All because we have a broken system
The older generations tell us that they have wisdom,
No, you're just as predictable as a well-oiled piston.

It's not quite right when there's an unwanted hand on her thigh
Or when all he can do is look down and cry
And no matter how hard they try and disguise it, they can't
So, they just wait until the next sunrise.

It's not quite right, can't we all get along?
And I'm no fool, life isn't a happy song
But how can it be so hard to see who's in the wrong?
This story does not need to go on for so long.

New Hue

My hair changes colour
with the seasons
No longer am I
burnt peach
Now I am living
a tangerine dream
Each new hue
an attempt to
leave you
behind

Each new shade
an attempt to
leave behind
the old me
With each season
I metamorphose
I transform
The winter has been
dark
My hair has shed
from the stress
Left traces of my
former self

Every time I
closed my eyes
you were all I saw
But spring is approaching
My hair is getting lighter
And as the trees start to
blossom
so
will
I

Hannah Petch

Breathing

My bedroom breathes with me; we
fall into a rhythm right for a pair. Books
stand to attention on their shelves, identity
apparent on walls, leftover crumbs of anorexia in the bed to be
   brushed away and made
irrelevant to all except the struggling hoover. Fake
plants because I've never been good at looking after living things, fairy
lights softening the blow of a hard day, shoes
to get me where I need to be, flowers –
a reminder of love, pictures
to show me I have never been alone and
I never will be.

Lucy Pettigrew

the things i am ~~not~~

as i caress my fingers
over my scarred and stretched skin,
i recite my flaws into my reflection.

skin too bumpy;
hips too wide;
tummy too round;
thighs not gappy enough;
~~not~~ enough.

my hair does not flow;
my lips do not sit plump on my face;
my body is not carved to fit the ideals;
my cheekbones do not cut glass;
~~not~~ enough.

self-love has never been my strong point;
i do not fit the ever-changing beauty standards
that society has forced upon me.
but maybe
just maybe
i am ~~not~~ enough.

i will learn to love myself,
though society will tell me not to.
i am many things;
i am whole, complete, loved, desired, needed.

maybe
just maybe

maybe

i am exactly who i am meant to be.

Katie Smith

Post-partum

@newmumfun: feel like I havent slept since we got back from the hospital
01:43 12/01/2019

@newmumfun:
4yo: what's that?
Me: coffee
4yo: can i have some?
Me: no its bad for you
4yo: why do you drink it?
Me: you.
09:43 14/02/2019

@newmumfun: for anyone thinking of having children, my youngest just spit up on my last clean shirt
13:04 16/02/2019

@newmumfun: just had to drop 4yo off at nursery for the first time. i'm sure i'll stop crying by the time he does his GCSEs
08:43 03/09/2019

@newmumfun: 4yo just asked me why i couldn't just put his sister back in my belly for a while to give us a break from the crying
09:20 08/09/2019

@newmumfun: leaving the flat for the last time today was bittersweet. can't wait to decorate the new place!
15:36 18/06/2020

@newmumfun: so glad i spent £500 on toys for Christmas so that my 5yo can play with the boxes they came in
07:56 25/12/2020

@newmumfun: bit of a rant so bear with me. if i had a pound for every time someones offered me advice i didn't ask for about raising

my children, i'd be able to afford the horse my 5yo has been asking for for weeks. keep your nose out and worry about your own life not mine. so frustrating to have people act like you have no clue, and it really leaves you doubting how good of a mother you actually are #leavemealone #theyrenotdeadyetarethey
20:58 06/03/2020

@newmumfun: is it bedtime yet?
10:42 10/03/2021

@newmumfun: being a mum is one of the hardest jobs in the world but its walking in to seeing your kids fast sleep on the sofa with the dog in between them both that makes it worth it #socute
17:05 30/09/2021

@newmumfun: 2yo just said her first word! "cup"! so exciting!
13:09 16/12/2021

@newmumfun: if i hear the word "why" one more time i'm gonna deafen myself
14:03 02/02/2022

@newmumfun: 6yo and 2yo arguing about 6yo breathing too much air #joysofparenthood #luckyme
18:08 16/09/2022

@newmumfun: 6yo has decided he wants to be a lizard when he's older. none of the parenting books prepared me for this
20:30 23/11/2022

@newmumfun: this will be the last tweet on this account. it's been a wild few years but my youngest starts nursery tomorrow and this feels like a good stopping point. when this all started i had just a newborn baby, a phone, and a sense of humour. there were honestly days when i couldn't have done it without you. i love you all. thank you for making these years even more special than they already would have been.
21:34 03/09/2023

Emily Stone

Day 372

I lean stiffly against the kitchenette counter as the boys bring the rest of the bags in from the minivan. The static caravan isn't big enough to sleep everyone; a couple of them will have to sleep on the sofas. I ask a quiet girl, whose name I think is Lauren, if I can take the other bed in the room she has already settled in. She smiles, nodding, but doesn't speak a word to me.

I return to the living area after putting my things away, and the driver beckons me over to sit next to him. I comply, taking the empty spot on the floor in the circle of murmurs. No one seems willing to talk over a whisper, as if they're afraid that we'll be found if they speak too loudly.

The driver's name is Harry. We had a few classes together in high school, but I wouldn't have thought he even knew my name until yesterday. His denim jeans and white button up shirt make no effort to hide his pointed elbows and knees. He still has his long, dirty blonde hair, hanging stringy over his shoulders. It was fashionable for men to grow out their hair before the Reform. It was considered rugged and daring; now most have cut it shorter like the time Before.

'You hungry?' he asks me.

'A little.'

'Is there a takeaway round here somewhere?' A few people jump at his question.

'There are a few shops around the corner,' mutters one of the boys. 'Should be something there.'

Harry unfolds his lanky limbs. 'I'll get us all something. Anyone coming?'

I get up. I don't know any of these people except him, and I don't think I can stand this quietness for much longer.

It's twilight. On our right as we exit the campsite, the sky is starless, empty. To the left, a tight navy-to-yellow haze hangs just above the horizon, a layer of pink slicing through it. I walk a little behind Harry, my head lowered. We come to a one-way bridge over a black, leaf-littered river, which has a little walkway to the left branching away from the road.

'Thank you,' I feel the need to say.

'What for?' He smiles crookedly and cocks his head to one side.

Our eyes meet for perhaps the first time, but I immediately look away. 'For picking me up yesterday and letting me join you. I know how hard it must be for them to suddenly have to trust a stranger.'

'*I* trust you. That should be enough for them, especially at a time like this. They just don't think *you* trust *them*.'

'I don't.'

'Oh.'

'You shouldn't take it personally.'

'Well, I wasn't going to leave you in the middle of the road. We had a spare seat and we ran right into you. They all understand my decision. You have nothing to worry about.'

We round the corner into a small town square, and that familiar smell fills my nose. It's like burnt wood and ash, laced with something else. These days it's the smell that follows you everywhere, through cities, towns, and even little hamlets like this. The only place you can get away from it completely is the countryside.

I don't mean country suburbs, a few miles from the city centre. I mean deep into the countryside. Where you can stand in the middle of the Yorkshire Moors or the Lake District and see nothing but green and gold fields around you, perhaps the odd farmhouse. Where the soot and rubble don't plague your eyes. Where you can remember that the world was once supposedly beautiful and forget that it isn't anymore.

I don't remember this place. I know that I must have been here before. But if I were to remember everywhere that I've been, every home that I... that *we* pillaged, every city that we burnt to the ground, I don't think even *I* could bare it.

There is a public house on either side of the road. The one on our side is brightly lit and filled with rowdy villagers, the scent of soaked beer mats and cigarettes bleeding into that constant smell of decimation. They're ignoring it. It makes me sick.

The one on the other side of the road has a broken clock hanging over the front door, suspended only by the rusted hinges of a bracket. The roof has completely collapsed in on itself and the tops of the walls have crumbled, if not from the Rampage, from being beaten by the weather over the past year.

I decide to sit on a bench outside the takeaway whilst Harry goes in. It seems to have taken me until now to notice how few people are around. There are no queues in either the pizza takeaway or the chip shop. I can just about remember a time when, on a Friday night like this, people would stand in lines so long they would lead out of the doors and onto the pavement, delivery bikes coming to and from restaurants in ridiculous numbers. Young people would stand, shivering in the cold, at bus stops or waiting for a taxi to take them to the nearest clubs and bars.

But now, even after all the time that has passed, only the bravest stay out late. Because *we* came in the night, and people are afraid that we will come again. So things are quiet. I like it this way.

'Horrible, isn't it?' Harry has appeared behind me, carrying six pizza boxes.

'What?' I frown, standing and taking three of the boxes from him.

'The village, it's ruined. Half of the shops have shut down. I was just chatting to a guy who works in there about it.'

Only half? I think to myself. We only managed to shut down half of the village businesses? It's no wonder the pub is full and people can go about their lives as if what happened a year ago was just another natural disaster that spannned the globe. We had one job to do, and if we had done it properly, there would be no public houses, no pizza takeaways, nothing to indicate that there had ever been a little hamlet here at all.

'That's why I can't stay anywhere for too long.' I don't realise that Harry is still speaking, but apparently he hasn't noticed my ignorance. 'I can't stand looking at places like this. I don't understand why it all happened.'

I know I shouldn't say anything. I could very well explain to Harry exactly why this *had* to happen and, if it had been done properly, it would have done the world a lot of good.

But the other three Horsemen have scattered. Perhaps they've given up. Perhaps they've even begun trying to rebuild the world that we broke. But when that thought crawls up my spine and tries to penetrate my skull, I shake it off into the road as a car passes by.

So I say the only thing I can, without lying. 'It could be worse.'

It *should* be worse.

Marian Stone

I am nature, and nature is me

As the sun glistens between the branches,
my eyes water and I take a breath.
The light is extraordinary.
A kaleidoscope, reflecting hundreds of
colours and patterns through the fingertips
of the trees. The leaves glow and glisten
and sparkle as they smile.

Most people find it chilling and a place
where you go to get lost.
But not I.
I come here to be found.

I find myself in the lone ghost orchid,
who hides from the sun and shelters
between the trees. I find myself hiding,
in between elderflower, blended in
out of sight but so clear in view. I hide
in the beams of the blinding golden sun
at sunrise. I take shelter in the grass
with the woodlouse and ants whom
have become my friends.

I don't come to the deep dark forest to
get lost. Not I.
I come here to be found.

To find myself and a reason to
live.

I find myself lying down in the wet moss
soaking up the sun, feeling
the soil in between my fingertips,
the sun burning my skin, the ants
crawling over my body.
The ghost orchid growing in me and
blooming.

I feel the soil running in between
my bones like blood. Ivy wrapping
around my organs like a race
it will never lose. Honeysuckle
weaving around my body
like a trap I welcome with an
open heart. I do not wander
in this forest like a lone cloud.

I race and fly like a flock of birds,
run like a pack of wolves.

This is where I belong, this is my
home. Nature welcomes me.

I am alive.
I am reborn.
I am nature, and nature is me.

Olivia Timmins

Live, My Darling Boy

Chapter 1: Smoke

A young couple lay together on the floor of their living room, in orange light with the curtains drawn. The wireless played static Jazz and the two began to melt into the song. Her, transforming into a sleeping Ella Fitzgerald and him, a tired Louis Armstrong. It was the kind of music that could only be truly appreciated if listened to in a quiet room, without the distraction of one's lover or a favoured book. But this was not a room that welcomed the observance of Jazz, there were distractions far greater than that. This was a room that seemed to curve into itself the way scarfs do in Winter, folded tightly but free from any knots or tangles.

The husband yawned and sat up to look upon his wife's naked body, a sight he agreed never to stop marvelling upon. She lay peacefully with her eyes closed, unaware, vulnerable and being loved too deeply. He studied her a moment longer before bringing her limp hand up to his lips and kissed each fingertip softly. Mr Taylor believed that there was an art to loving his wife and looking over her whilst she slept was one he took pride in keeping to himself.

'Winifred darling?' he whispered, careful not to take her away from too good a dream. Usually a heavy sleeper, it seemed the only thing to wake Mrs Taylor was the sound of her husband's voice calling her "darling", for she did not want to miss whatever words followed.

Winifred opened her eyes and blinked slowly with upturned eyebrows and parted lips. 'Yes Jered darling? Are you in need of your wife to resolve yet another one of your unresolvable thoughts?' she asked teasingly.

Unsure of what to reply, Jered began to trace his fingers lightly around Winifred's collar bones and up towards the side of her face. Winifred rested her flushed cheek into her husband's palm and exhaled. Silence followed, a pause that neither one of them wanted to end. Breaking away from his daydream, Jered diverted his gaze into Winifred's eyes. His face weakened; as every good husband knows, the only weakness a man has pleasure in having is the one brought on by the love he has for his wife. He pulled her closer and scooped her into his arms, 'My wife... my life...'

Chapter 2: Fire

Fact is so often more frightening than fiction and the simple fact was this: the country was now at war and Mr. Taylor had been deployed to fight in France against the German army. Men left their homes with light in their eyes and victory on their lips, in freshly ironed uniforms and slicked back hair, promising their families of a safe homecoming. After tearfully waving off Mr. Taylor at King's Cross station, Winifred Taylor returned to their home and felt an emptiness settle in her stomach as she closed the door behind her. She stood still, clinging to her handbag with wide, sad eyes and afraid to step into her home, alone.

*

It was now December, and Jered sat with his back against a cold soil landscape, gun in arms and a pencil in his pocket. He looked up and squinted one eye in search of constellations he could recognise, but the clouds had made the sky murky and foreign. He looked down and exhaled, noticing the white fog of his breath enter the darkness, it reminded him of Winifred. Dipping a hand into his pocket for the pencil and his last blank sheet of paper, Jered returned to his regular post to write a letter to his wife.

Chapter 3: Ash

Mrs. Taylor stood in a nightgown at her bathroom sink and began to bathe her face. After patting her cheeks with a towel, she studied herself closely in the mirror and caressed her jaw delicately.

'Oh goodness, surely not,' she whispered to herself. It was to be this day that Winifred Taylor found her first grey hair. A world of war without her husband had aged her like one of the many ornaments she had scattered around their home, surprisingly well but not without dust. Undoing the pin rolls in her hair, she walked out of the bathroom before a knock at the door startled her. She'd thought it be a letter from Jered, having not received one in a little over a week.

She wrapped her robe around her shoulders and quickly ran down the stairs before noticing that no letters had come through the letterbox, and instead, the silhouette of two men stood through the frosted glass of the front door. She paused and clung to the banister tightly, suddenly motionless and inhaling thick breaths of air. A lump in her throat started to swell and her fingers began to shake and, for the life of her, Mrs. Taylor could not move forward to answer the door. She closed her eyes and imagined it was Jered on the other side, with open arms and without wounds or any sign of torment. She was becoming long lost in the thought of it before a second knock woke her. She wrapped her fingers around the door handle before opening it and caving instantly to her knees at the sight of two officers holding a telegram. Her cry was not the sound of a wife, or even a mother or young infant in distress; it was the scream of an animal howling in the night.

MRS. TAYLOR,

THE SECRETARY OF WAR DIRECTS ME TO EXPRESS HIS DEEP REGRET THAT YOUR HUSBAND, 2nd LIEUTENANT JERED WILLIAM TAYLOR, WAS KILLED IN ACTION IN DEFENSE OF HIS COUNTRY ON 2nd JANUARY IN FRANCE. LETTER FOLLOWS.

THE ADJUTANT GENERAL

The two officers began to help Winifred to her feet, but she refused. If Winifred could not stand, how could she live? One of the officers knelt to her level and held her hand, 'Please, take this, your husband wrote a letter he had not yet posted. It was found by one of his friends in his pocket, it is addressed to you. Please Madam, come to your feet.' She looked down at the letter in the officer's hand, her face weakening at the sight of Jered's handwriting and the crumpled condition of the paper.

In a daze and holding the letter by her fingertips, Winifred closed the door and turned to the living room and headed towards her regular chair. The moment she sat, the sun crept through the window's glass, pouring an orange light into the room and upon Winifred's lap. She gazed towards the glass until she heard a sound that made her flinch, dropping Jered's letter onto the carpet.

There were not many things that disrupted Mrs. Taylor from her gazes, except the sound of her husband's voice calling her "Darling", for she did not want to miss whatever words followed. She picked up the letter and let it rest in her palm, before opening the seal carefully.

Tears rolled down to her face and over her lips before she paused and smiled, 'Yes, my Darling Boy?'

Maia Tudor

Debris

The crooked, old lady rarely moved from the waterside once she dumped down amidst the rubbish and wreckage that drifted ashore. Some days, she eased herself to a spot of clean sand, always directly on top of it, others, she'd ruffle her wrinkled hand through the plastic and pebbles of styrofoam, desperately trying to find a clean patch, but rarely able to.

She would sit from the early turquoise morning to the pastel blue afternoon, simply staring at the waves rolling in from the sea, sometimes crashing against the beach when pelting rain fell from the gabbro-tinted clouds.

The girl would find her in a raincoat and a bright yellow Sou'wester stuck to her head like glue. Not even the harshest gale could tear it from her head and whip it into the air for the clouds to swallow. Often, she'd find her in a floral summer dress.

She was always there, the old lady, enchanted by the rubbish and whatever else the locals dumped on the beach.

With thick boots, the girl trudged her way along the rubbish-laden ground, morose mood tugging at her features, at the thought of more plastic and wreckage drifting ashore. It was hard enough to walk as it was. She didn't need more garbage to make it more difficult to walk to school. It was the first day of the semester, and the wind was forcing her carefully braided hair to come undone.

She could taste salt on her tongue, the wind making her teeth clatter.

Swapping the song on her iPhone to *Sedona* by Houndmouth, she passed the lady and spotted a worn and torn book in her hands. She was a crooked, old thing, hunched over the novel as if about to push it into her stomach and let her intestines devour it.

The girl stuck her hand in her bag and picked up the sandwich her mother had made her before she was ushered out of the house. Wrapped in cling film, the sandwich didn't look particularly appetising, but the girl was hungry, and unless she planned to be in a sour mood for the entire day, she had to eat.

She unwrapped the film from the sandwich and chucked it somewhere amongst all the rubbish on the ground. It wasn't like anyone ever would notice, anyways.

On the second day of the semester, the girl startled when she passed the wrinkly lady, who chirped, 'You're here early.' She spoke on outbreath, the wind tearing at her words, whipping them into the air.

She was splattered with white pebbles of styrofoam. She looked like a dalmatian starting to grow into its spots, her black woollen coat attracting the pebbles like glue.

Shuffling on her feet, the girl grasped her wrist behind her back. 'On my way to school.' Her denim coat was already attracting the white pebbles, and she dreaded every second she had to stand there, peering out at the open sea, grimacing at the plastic lulling against her exposed ankles.

A book rested on the lady's lap. There was a dead, yellow bird on the cover.

The girl frowned.

The lady petted the spot beside her, a patch of clean sand, but the girl remained upright, eyes thinning at the twitching, gnarly hand. Veins snarled around the wrinkles.

The End of Nature, the girl read in her head. The title of the book. *How fun*, she thought drily when the crooked lady spoke again. She was running late for her lecture, but didn't want to be rude either.

'I remember reading this nearly thirty years ago,' she said, shaking her head. 'Thought it was rubbish.'

A small, tired smile curled on the girl's lips. The kind she had to force.

'But then,' she sighed and gripped a tiny, white styrofoam pearl, 'first it was a few crisp packets and instant barbecues. Was a lovely little beach back then,' she said and nodded at the sandwich the girl held in her hand. 'Used to be some tidewrack washing ashore every now and then, not plastic.'

Red tinted the girl's cheeks, creeping up her neck and temples like a rising thermometer. She could not for the life of her remember a time when the beach hadn't looked like a dumpsite.

'I used to sit here with my husband,' the old lady said and stroked the patch of clean sand, running it through her fingers. 'Long before it looked like this.' With a sad, closed-lipped smile, she said, 'I couldn't not come here, even though the world changed.'

Was it really a clean beach before? the girl wondered.

'I need to get to my lecture,' she said and gestured to the town in the distance.

The lady cackled. 'Of course. Of course. On you go,' she said and waved her hand at the girl, ushering her away.

Leaving her to her own business, the girl glanced back, chewing her lips raw while trudging through the plastic and rubbish. *Clean beach*, she thought, and her brows narrowed.

The old lady leaned back in the sand, still stroking the patch of clean sand.

Every day after, the girl would stop by the old lady, no matter the weather. On the days when it rained, she tilted her brolly to shield the crooked creature sitting in the sand. On the days of sun, she would share a piece of her sandwich, quick to put her new lunchbox back in her bag.

On one particular day, the girl bounced toward the old lady, tender-hearted and insecure when she held out a piece of paper. It had a picture of the beach. But there was no plastic. No rubbish. She'd found it in the library, copied it.

Handing the flyer to the old lady, the girl pointed to the text beneath the photo.

This Friday 5pm.
Make the Beach Great Again!

'The town will come and help you clean it up. It's time to make a change.'

With a sweet, wobbly smile, the old lady tilted her head back, the Sou'wester flopping in the sea breeze. A silver lining threatened to spill some tears from her eyes, but the girl merely swatter her hand at her.

'It's time for the town to change,' she said, and the old lady gave a curt nod, the slip of paper pressed tightly to her chest.

Silje Marie Tunes

Seasons of Life

Every good gift and every perfect gift is from above, and cometh down from the Father of lights, with whom is no variableness, neither shadow of turning. Of his own will begat he us with the word of truth, that we should be a kind of firstfruits of his creatures.

James 1:17-18

*

September 25th.

You never forget that moment you are told something that alters your life. She was dead. The only family he knew had been taken away. Ripped away from life, the life she made for herself and this little boy. Everything was gone. No more of her chicken soup because no matter where he goes they never seem to do it just right. No more Shema because no matter how hard he tried he never quite got the grasp of Hebrew.

No more of the sound of her voice as she reads out loud his choice of story from the bookshelf. Overwhelmed, he grabs the first one he finds, sits next to what was her chair and reads aloud for her: 'Is not this a true autumn day? Just the still melancholy that I love – that makes life and nature harmonise. The birds are consulting about their migrations, the trees are putting on the hectic or the pallid hues of decay, and begin to strew the ground, that one's very footsteps may not disturb the repose of earth and air, while they give us a scent that is a perfect anodyne to the restless spirit. Delicious autumn! My very soul is wedded to it, and if I were a bird I would fly about the earth seeking the successive autumns.'

*

December 27th.

Christmas had passed, the presents opened, the dinner eaten. Now there was less to do, however the stress from looking after two overly excited children was exhausting. Who knew 5 year olds were so energetic? Taking a few minutes for herself she looks through the window and sees the soft white flakes falling down from the sky above. Having not seen this happen in over four years, she rushes to the girls and dresses them in the largest, warmest coats and proceeds to go outside. The two little girls, having not seen this before were confused at first glance. 'The snow doesn't give a soft white damn whom it touches.' Yet they eventually see the wonders that it brings and further begin to play experiencing one thing every British child should. 'A snowball in the face is surely the perfect beginning to a lasting friendship.'

*

March 11th.

Three days to go until the due date. Everyone is excited for the arrival but her. The thought of the birth is her biggest fear. This pregnancy hasn't been easy and after the ordeal last time all her hopes and joy have gone into this baby. Her husband has not long finished the nursery, what was once baby blue walls in a room no one dared to enter is now a bright yellow sunshine. Each time she sees the walls her fears start to mellow ways and the promise of this new life … her new light just feels slightly like everything will be better once again. 'What I need is the dandelion in the spring. The bright yellow that means rebirth instead of destruction. The promise that life can go on, no matter how bad our losses. That it can be good again.'

*

June 6th.

June 6th, the perfect day for a day like this. They say when you marry in June you'll be a bride all your life. As he stands there anxiously waiting all he can think about is her. The string quartet starts to play the bridal march and he feels a small bead of sweat form on his brow. As he goes to wipe it away in a panic there she is. Starting at the end of the aisle, perfect, his sunshine and his happiness. All doubt that he held beforehand vanished away with one look at her eyes, the shift mix of blue, green and gold reflecting in the sunlight. This is his life now beginning all over again. 'And so with the sunshine and the great bursts of leaves growing on the trees, just as things grow in fast movies, I had that familiar conviction that life was beginning over again with the summer.'

*

To every thing there is a season, and a time to every purpose under the heaven

Ecclesiastes 3:1

Credits to George Eliot, e.e. cummings, Markus Zusak, Suzanne Collins and F. Scott Fitzgerald

Meghan Venus

The Stream

I am rooted but I flow, through fields and over pastures, by the towns
   and past the cities,
      I travel the void,
expand myself miles,   millennia,   eons.
I amass,   then fracture,   scope, then restrain.   I devour
                  great continents

as I sit in the churchyard tracing my fingers   along
        the regurgitated stone.

I am a bird;   I fly the furthest distance.
         I flow in great paths across the sky and
     delve through the deepest   oceans.
I sing and I call –   hear my tune echo back.
      I migrate   feather my nest,
   in the tree,   in your yard   in Dorset,
      each winter.

    I drown in every perpetual second,
      yet I live a thousand lives more than you.
       I wander the moor, sail to the island –
I need to live and I long to
         die –
as I rest my head fitfully on my pillow,   in my bed, in this cottage
           in Surrey.

          I am always alone
         yet surrounded by faces.
I sing great operas and revel   in the   silence
    for the crowd is large,   made up of myself.

I compose vast poems; my prose is a
       sentence.
I laugh.

I cry.
　　I love.
　　　　　I long.

It seems I live in eternal stasis,
　　　though I move like a slipstream over the
　　　　　earth.
My eyes are mirrors,　　　　　but my soul is a
　　　　　　　　　　fissure.
　　　I am unsure whether I am alive or whether　　I am dead.

　　Agony sings　　　and happiness is full of moroseness –
　　　　it will not speak to me for　　I have offended it so.
It pines and it burns, perishes in the blackness
as I pass　　　time freezes – it hates me –　　because I left it

　　　　　alone.

　　　　　I sit and I wonder　　the dawn growing grainy,
I slumber and wake
　　　　　fifty years in the past.
　　　　　　　　I yearn to travel
　　　　　　　but will stay here forever,
　　　　　time passes,
　　　　shadows growing and shrinking,
　　leaves falling and budding on this perpetual
earth.

*With credit to Virginia Woolf, Walt Whitman, E.E. Cummings and
William Shakespeare.*

　　　　　　　　　　Courtney Wakelin

Lunar

the blood is brown sludge against the white cotton of her
briefs and the bell rings and it's time for double maths where
she sits next to Lucy and they (think it's a) struggle to solve
what XX is but elsewhere a girl a woman a wife a mother a sister
huddles in a hut and can't touch dairy or step inside until her time
is done and the nights are cold and in the morning light their blood
is what Victoria wished for each month instead of pregnancy and
the despair each Tudor wife felt when she saw red drops instead of
a red head of a son and when their linens were washed and dried
their bloodstained whites are the rags the washerwoman uses
to staunch her own blood from dripping down her thighs as under
the burning sun she picks sugar cane with a child on her back
and sorrow in her heart that the first time she bled it was after
the overseer and that child is long gone and still the blood trickles

Jessica White

Acknowledgements

Editorial Team 2020
Olivia De Marco (Project Team Leader), Jess Shepherd (Sub Team Leader), Meghan Venus-Bradley (Sub Team Leader). Charlotte Ashley, Tod Barnbrook, Emma Brimelow, Hannah Burgess, Grace Burrill, Esther Henderson, Laura Kirkwood, Anissa Maloney, Hannah Matthews, Liv Osborne, Katherine Parker, Natasha Pavis, Amy Power, Abbi Smith, Olivia Timmins, Maia Tudor, Belén Vargas, Ethan Zaccardelli, Lorna Zurek.

Events and Marketing Team 2020
Piaras Hale (Project Team Leader). Hayley Alcock, Christopher Allen, Sophie Barrett, Octavia Lena Bettis, Drew Boulton, Elizabeth Colcombe, Skye Cottingham, Francesca Ivinson, Kate Morgan, Bobby Muscart, Beth Nicholson, Laurel Nisbet, Emily Reeves.

Blog and Podcasting Team 2020
Alyssa Cope (Project Team Leader), Lucy Morton (Sub-team Leader), Rachel Wainwright (Sub-team Leader). Lottie Brooke, Olivia Fyfe, Chloe Green, Emily Green, Ben Mcdonald, Myles Palmer, Megan Tinker.

Cover Design: Bronte Rockliff